GRAND
DAY OUT

Songs and rhymes
for active grandparenting

Compiled by Sheena Roberts
Illustrated by Rachel Fuller
Performed by Playsongs People

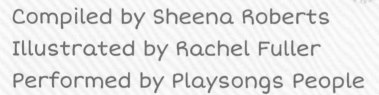

Stephen Chadwick, James Fagan, Kevin Graal, Steve Grocott,
Sandra Kerr, Nancy Kerr, Giles Leaman, Janet Russell, Leon
Rosselson, Debbie Sanders, Kaye Umansky, Rick Wilson, Tom Wright

PLAYSONGS PUBLICATIONS · LONDON

For Great
Grandad David
and for Sarah

First published in Great
Britain by Playsongs
Publications Limited.
playsongs.co.uk

© 2021 Playsongs
Publications Ltd

ISBN: 978-0-9517112-5-5

Printed in the UK by Ashley
House Printing Company.
Sustainability: printed
using green energy
on FSC and carbon
balanced paper and
card, using vegan-
friendly vegetable
inks and non-plastic
bio-gloss cover finish.
Fully compostable,
biodegradable and
recyclable.

Text © 2021
Sheena Roberts.
Illustrations © 2021
Rachel Fuller.
Graphic design by
Jocelyn Lucas.
Sound engineering by
3D Music, and
Powered Flight.
Post production by
3D Music.

GRAND THANKYOUS

Many people have given their energy, their ideas, and their creativity to the making of this *Grand Playsongs* series. Particular thanks are due to Kaye Umansky, without whom I would never have started, and to Stephen Chadwick, without whom I would never have finished. Also to:

~ everyone in **Playsongs People** for their musical creativity, their fun-filled performances, their voices and their many other instrumental skills: Stephen Chadwick, James Fagan, Kevin Graal, Steve Grocott, Sandra Kerr, Nancy Kerr, Giles Leaman, Helen MacGregor, Janet Russell, Leon Rosselson, Debbie Sanders, Kaye Umansky, Rick Wilson, Tom Wright, and guest vocalist, Great Grandad David (*Puffing Billies*);

~ illustrator, Rachel Fuller, whose colours and characters warm every page, and to Joc Lucas for her graphic design, which wraps everything together;

~ Helen MacGregor and all the many readers and contributors, who checked the drafts, recalled their favourite childhood songs, taught me others, corrected my mistakes and jollied the books along: Charlie, Jake, Marco, Tim, Linda, Kevin, Heather, Tamar, Rachel, Joyce, Elizabeth, Jo, Polly, Sarah, Mary, Emily, Victoria, Margareta, Jody, Cina, Bethan, Abigail, Bea, Anni, Linda, Etain, Elizabeth, Charlotte, Danielle, Ali, Vicki and Mawadda.

WORDS AND MUSIC

• 3 *Granny can make me grin*, 12 *Off to the park with Grandpa*, 30 *Hugs*: words by **Kaye Umansky** © 2021.

• 6 *All by yourself* © **Leon Rosselson**.

• 10 *To market to market* words by Sheena Roberts, with music composed and arranged by **Stephen Chadwick** and with additional jig contributed and performed by **Nancy Kerr**. Arrangement © 2021 Playsongs Publications Ltd.

• 23 *Off we go! (The pram song)* © 2021 **Steve Grocott**.

• 28 *Ice cream (I scream, you scream, we all scream for ice cream)* by **Howard Johnson**, **Billy Moll**, **Robert A King** © 1927 Shapiro Bernstein & Co Inc. Administered by Faber Music Ltd on behalf of Reservoir Media Management, Inc. All rights reserved. (Original verse lyric adapted by permission.)

• 29 *Morningtown Ride* by Malvina Reynolds © Amadeo Music (ASCAP). All rights reserved. Used by permission.

• 1 *Grand hello* (words), 4 *Google translate* (words), 5 *Gran Band* (adapted words), 7 *One two on with your shoe* (words), 9 *Miss Mary Mac* (adapted words), 11 *Teddy in the window* (words and music), 13 *Kokoleoko* (Ghana) (adapted words), 14 *Bumble bees* (words), 17 *Wheeee PLOP* (words), 26 *Sons of the sea* (verses 3 and 4, words), the English word-setting of 24 *Grandpa's donkey* (Lebanon) contributed by Kevin Graal, 27 *Donkey riding* (adapted words) by **Sheena Roberts** © 2021 Playsongs Publications Ltd.

• *Author unknown/public domain:* 2 Handy pandy (UK); 8 Got me a job/We're off to the shops/Left right whoopty doo (UK); 15 See saw Marjory Daw (UK), and *Obadiah do* (chorus) *(Swing me higher, Obadiah)* words **AE Rick**, music **Maurice Scott** (public domain); 16 Michael Finnigin (Ireland); 18 Six little ducks (North America); 19 Puffing Billies (England); 20 We're off in a motor car (England); 21 *Daisy Bell* by **Harry Dacre** (1892, public domain); 22 Clip clop clip clop (UK); 25 *I do like to be beside the seaside* by **John H Glover-Kind** (1907, public domain).

All musical arrangements © 2021 Playsongs Publications Ltd. All audio in *Playsongs Grand Day Out* is published and distributed under licence from PRS-MCPS

Every effort has been made to trace and acknowledge owners of copyright lyrics reprinted in this publication. If any right has been omitted, the publishers offer their apologies and following written notification will rectify any print omissions on reprint.

CONTENTS

1 GRAND HELLO

Daddy's daddy is here today,
We'll sing, Hello,
And shout, HOORAY!
Daddy's daddy is here today,
He's my Grandad David.

Mummy's mummy is here today,
We'll clap our hands
And shout, HOORAY!
Mummy's mummy is here today,
She's my Granny Tina.

Mamma's mamma is here today,
We'll zoom round the room
And shout, HOORAY!
Mamma's mamma is here today,
She's my Nonna Maria.

Vati's vati is here today,
We'll swing from the lamps
And shout, HOORAY!
Vati's vati is here today,
He's my Opa Stefan.

GRAND HELLO
Tune: The mulberry bush

Sing your hellos to each other and shout HOORAY to celebrate a 'Grand' arrival. Change all the names to your own. Even just in English there are so many variants of grandmother and grandfather.

HANDY PANDY

For babies, hold a treat in one open palm and as you say the rhyme, swap it from one to the other. Turn your fists over and let baby find the treat. With toddlers and little children, hide both hands behind your back.

GRANNY CAN MAKE ME GRIN

Tune: Here we go looby loo

A song for hugs, jumps, dancing and more hugs.

2 HANDY PANDY

Handy pandy
Sugar candy,
Win or lose,
Win or lose,
Which one will you choose?

3 GRANNY CAN MAKE ME GRIN

Granny can make me grin
Whatever the mood I'm in,
Yes she can, she can, my gran!
Granny can bring the sunshine in.

Granny can make me jump
Whenever I'm in a grump,
Yes she can, she can, my gran!
Granny can make me jump.

Granny can make me dance
Whenever she gets the chance,
Yes she can, she can, my gran!
Granny can make me dance.

Granny, come in and play,
Granny, come in and stay,
Say you can, you can, you can!
Granny, you make it a sunny day.

4 GOOGLE TRANSLATE

Goo, goo, goo ~ Goo, goo, goo,
Goo, google, goo ~ Goo, google, goo,
In google translate I say, 'How do you do?'
In google reply you say, 'Fine ~ thank you'
Goo, google, goo ~ Goo, google, goo.

5 GRAN BAND

I am the Music Gran, I come from far away,
And I can play. What can you play?
I play the tum-drum ~
Tum tiddle-um, tiddle-um tum-tum,
Tum tum tum, tum tum tum,
Tum tiddle-um, tiddle-um tum-tum,
Oh what lovely fun.

I am the Music Gran, I come from far away,
And I can play. What can you play?
I play the shin-bone ~
Parp parp, out and in ...
What a lovely din!

I am the Music Gran, I come from far away,
And I can play. What can you play?
I play accordiarm ~
Accordiarms go stretch and squeeze ...
What a lovely wheeze!

All together now!
(Hullabaloo free for all ~ finish with an accordiarm hug)

GOOGLE TRANSLATE
Tune: Three blind mice
Sing hello to a tiny baby in their language. Sing slowly and with lots of eye contact.

GRAN BAND
Tune: I am the music man
Sit a baby or toddler outwards on your knee. Pat their 'tum-drum'; hold a foot to 'slide' a shin-bone out and in for a trombone; hold their hands in yours and hug your arms around them, out and in, to stretch and squeeze your accordion. Dance them in your arms in the last verse.

Bigger children can air play the instruments.

6 ALL BY YOURSELF

You can put your coat on,
You can put your coat on,
You can put your coat on,
All by yourself!
  All by yourself,
  You're a big girl now,
  You can do it
  All by yourself!

Naila can do her buttons up ...
All by herself.
  All by herself,
  She's a big girl now,
  She can do it
  All by herself.

Joe can put his boots on ...
All by himself ...

Chiara can get in the
  pushchair ...

ALL BY YOURSELF

What can your grand toddler do all by themselves to get ready for going out?

Great Grandad, Leon, songwriter, says:

'I don't remember actually writing *All by yourself*. I just sang it as I encouraged my daughter, Ruth (now 50), to put herself to bed. It just sort of sang itself.'

It's a song which just sort of sings itself in all kinds of moments of cajolery or celebration with a small child ~ you can do it all by yourselves.

ONE TWO
Start the outing
with a zippy
number rhyme.

MARCHING
MEDLEY
For two grown
ups holding
hands with a
toddler between.

~ *Got me a job*:
step left foot first.
~ *We're off to
the shops*: the
second line is
a fun, stepping
pattern, then on
line four ~ swing
your toddler up
and 'AWAY'.
~ *Whoopty doo*:
whichever foot
leads the march,
swap to the other
with a skip on
'Whoopty doo',
eg start on the
left and skip 'left
right left' onto
your right foot
first. Babes-
in-arms love
the bounce in
your feet and
toddlers love to
have a go.

7 ONE TWO

One two ~
   on with your shoe,
Three four ~
   jump to the door,
Five six ~
   zipper to fix,
Seven eight ~
   wait by the gate!
Nine ten ~
   I say when_____
We're off, we're off
   so clear the way,
We're off for the whole
   of the day.

8 MARCHING MEDLEY

Got me a job for twenty-nine bob
But I left ~ left ~ left right left,
But I left right left!
   We're off to the shops whatever the weather,
   A-forward back and a side together!
   My hat! My coat! My collar! My cane!
   A-one! A-two! And AWAY down the lane!
Left, right, left, right, left, right,
Whoopty doo!
Right, left, right, left, right, left,
Whoopty doo!

9 MISS MARY MAC

Miss Mary Mac Mac Mac
All dressed in black black black
With silver buttons buttons buttons
All down her back back back.

She asked her gramp gramp gramp
For a first class stamp stamp stamp
To send the elephant elephant elephant
To the top of the lamp lamp lamp.

She told her nan nan nan
To hold her hand hand hand,
So they could stand stand stand
On the elephant's back back back.

They climbed so high high high
They touched the sky sky sky
And they didn't come back back back
Till they learned to fly_____back!

MISS MARY MAC
Sing it as you hold your toddler's hand for wall-walking, climbing and balancing. 'Fly' your toddler back down to land.

TO MARKET TO
MARKET

We've put a
twist in this
traditional
knee-bouncing
rhyme which
usually goes:

*To market
to market
to buy a fat pig,
Home again
home again,
jiggedy jig.*

Ours is a dance
rhyme.

Babes-in-arms
love to feel
rhythm through
your body as you
move and dance.

When a little baby
lies on his back,
the arms get
moving and
legs kick in
the air, and as
soon as he's
standing he's
bouncing!

10 TO MARKET TO MARKET

To market to market, forgotten the list,
Home again, home again, dancing the twist.

To market to market to buy a blue mango,
Home again, home again, dancing the tango.

To market to market to buy mashed banana,
Home again, home again, dancing to bhangra.

To market to market to sit in a cafe,
Home again, home again, dancing to reggae.

To market to market to buy a pink wig,
Home again, home again, dancing a jig.

To market to market to buy a high shelf,
If you want anymore you can rhyme it yourself!

11 TEDDY IN THE WINDOW

Teddy in the window on display,
How do we know how much to pay?
Is there a label, can you see?
Where oh where can the label be?
Well it's not on his chest,
Though that would be the best,
And it's not on his head,
His hat is there instead.

Well it's not on his nose,
As you might suppose
And it's not on his ear,
We can say it loud and clear.
Well it's not on his knee,
We can all agree!
And it's not on his tummy
Cos that would be so gummy ~
A label on his tummy!
Teddy in the window on display,
How do we know how much to pay?
Is there a label, can you see?
Where oh where can the label be?

(spoken:)

Well, where is it? Where can it be?
It's not on his chest, and not on his head,
It's not on his nose, and not on his ear,
It's not on his knee, and not on his tummy,
And it's certainly not on his face ~
We've looked all over the place!
Then a little voice sang ~

I am the teddy on display,
I can tell you how much to pay,
There's no label you can see,
Cos this little bear is yours for free.
I am a ted that's all alone,
All I want is a loving home,
All I want is a friend like you,
A cuddle and a hug and that ~ will ~ do!

TEDDY IN THE WINDOW

Sway a little baby on your knee and tap or tweak the parts of the body as they're mentioned.

With bigger babies and toddlers, have fun searching all over them for a 'label'.

Put a sticker on yourself for them to find when you sing 'Where oh where can the label be?'

GRAND
TIME AT THE PARK

12 OFF TO THE PARK

I'm off to the park with Grandpa,
To see what we can see!
The ducks are in the duck pond,
The birds are in the tree.

And when we reach the playground,
A go-on-the-swing for me,
I'm off to the park with Grandpa,
To see what we can see!

OFF TO THE PARK

Bounce baby in your arms as you stride out, or swing a toddler along between two of you.

KOKOLEOKO

'Kokoleoko' is 'cockadoodle doo' in Ghana. It's the sound for waking and getting going, wherever you are. Sing the song gently to wake a sleepy baby or toddler after a nap, or with lots of energy to get everyone out to play, out to the market, out to see a friend, out to the playgroup, or out to the park.

BUMBLE BEES

Crouch or sit down. Firmly hold baby under her arms with both your hands. Rise and fly her up above your head. Tip her forwards to touch foreheads, followed by a kiss.

13 KOKOLEOKO

Kokoleoko, baby, koleoko,
Kokoleoko, baby, koleoko.
Kokoleoko, baby, koleoko,
Kokoleoko, baby, koleoko.
  Isla, wakey, Isla,
  Isla, wakey, koleoko.

Wake up, baby, it's time to go,
Kokoleoko, let's go out and play.
Wake up, baby, it's time to go,
Kokoleoko, let's go out and play.
  Robbie, wakey, Robbie ...

Out to the playground, let's have some fun,
Kokoleoko, let's go out and play.
Out to the playground, come on, let's run,
Kokoleoko, let's go out and play.
  Debbie, wakey, Debbie ...

Kokoleoko, baby, koleoko ...

14 BUMBLE BEES

Buzzy buzzy bumble bees,
Flying UP in the breeze,
Heads down, bums up,
Supping from a flower cup!

15 SEE SAW ~ OBADIAH DO

See saw Marjory Daw,
Johnny has got a new master,
He shall earn but a penny a day
Because he can't work any faster.

Jump jump penny a lump,
Jenny has got a new master,
She shall earn but a penny a day
Because she can't jump any faster.

Swing me just a little bit higher,
Obadiah, do,
Swing me just a little bit higher,
and I'll love you.
Hold me on and I'll never fall,
Swing me over the garden wall,
Just a little bit higher, Obadiah, do.

Roll roll toad in the hole,
Joey has got a new master,
He shall earn but a penny a day,
Because he can't roll any faster.

Swing swing cardboard and string,
Yasmin has got a new master,
She shall earn but a penny a day
Because she can't swing any faster.

Swing me just a little bit higher ...

SEE SAW
A workhouse song, turned playsong with a perfect rhythm for the swings ~ or for jumping, or a roley poley over ~ and a see-saw.

OBADIAH DO
Today's grandparents may remember this from the TV revival of music hall, *The Good Old Days*, which ran from the 1950s to the 70s. But their own grandparents may have known it in their youth, singing along at a real 1900s music hall. A stage swing swung out over the audience, risquély revealing Obadiah's beloved's underwear.

MICHAEL FINNIGIN

After a mishap, cheer up a little one: jump them up, dust them down and 'beginigin' just like Michael Finnigin.

16 MICHAEL FINNIGIN

There was an old man called Michael Finnigin,
He fell down and bumped his chinigin,
Jumped right up and rubbed it goodigin,
Cheer up, Michael Finnigin, beginigin.

There was an old man called Michael Finnigin,
Climbed a tree and barked his shinigin,
Took off several yards of skinigin,
Jump up, Michael Finnigin, beginigin.

There was an old man called Michael Finnigin,
He fell down agin and aginigin,
Picked himself up and grinned a grinigin,
Good old Michael Finnigin.

WHEEEE PLOP

Tune: The bear went over the mountain

Sing as your toddler climbs the steps of a slide ~ speeding up and slowing down to match their progress. 'Wheee PLOP' as they slide down. Dolly, or train, or Nanna can play too.

17 WHEEEE PLOP

Isla climbed up to the mountain top,
Isla climbed up to the mountain top,
Isla climbed up to the mountain top,
And WHEEEEEEEEEEE PLOP!

Dolly climbed up to the mountain top ...

Train chugged up to the mountain top ...

Nanna climbed up to the mountain top ...

18 SIX LITTLE DUCKS

Six little ducks that I once knew,
Granny ducks, mammy ducks, baby ducks too.
But the one little duck with a feather on his back,
He led the others with his 'Quack quack quack,
Quack quack quack, quack quack quack,'
He led the others with his 'Quack quack quack'.

Down to the river they would go,
Wibble wobble, wibble wobble to and fro.
But the one little duck with a feather on his back,
He led the others with his 'Quack quack quack' ...

Home from the river they would come,
Wibble wobble, wibble wobble, ho-hum-hum!
But the one little duck with
a feather on his back,
He led the others with his
'Quack quack quack' ...

SIX LITTLE
DUCKS
Hands behind
your back,
everyone.
Put palms
together, and
waggle them
side to side like
tail feathers.
Waddle home,
taking turns to
be the leader,
waggling tail
feathers and
going 'Quack
quack quack'.

Or make up
fingerplay
actions for the
words.

GRAND
GETTING ABOUT

19 PUFFING BILLIES

Now we're at the station,
Early in the morning,
See the little Puffing Billies
All in a row.
Daddy's on the engine,
Turns a little handle,
Puff!—Puff!—Puff!—Puff!
Off we go.

PUFFING BILLIES

Great Grandad David remembered learning this when he was four years old in 1924. A fellow passenger on the train from Exeter to Dawlish taught him the song, as their steam engine puffed them along the coast. Over ninety years later he sang it for his baby great grand daughter.

This and the following songs are knee riders as well as fun to sing on any journey.

28 ICE CREAM

Jelly babies
Sugar mice
Barley sugar
Li-quo-rice,
I know something nicer in the freezer
   (the freezer).
Dolly mixtures
Walnut whip
Love hearts,
I say toodle-pip!
You know something nicer in the freezer
   (the freezer).

Sherbert fountains, chocolate buttons,
Highland coo chews,
These are lovely but
I've got some far better news.

Aniseed and
Ginger creams
Flying saucers,
Keep them dreams,
We know something nicer in the freezer
   (the freezer).

I scream, you scream,
We all scream for ice cream. Rah! Rah! Rah!
   (Rather have an ice cream any old time)
Tuesdays, Mondays,
We all scream for sundaes. Ssss! Oooh! Ahhh!
   (Raspberry ripple and a ninety nine!)
   Boola-boola, sarsparoolla.
   We've got some chocolate ~ I'll take vanoola.
I scream, you scream,
We all scream for ice cream. Rah! Rah! Rah!
   (Arctic roll up and stand in line)
      (Instrumental)
         I scream, you scream ...
         Hal-le-luuuuuuuuuuuuu-ya!
         (Knickerbocker glory halleluya!)

Jelly babies, sugar mice ...

I scream, you scream,
We all scream for ice cream. Rah! Rah! Rah!
   (Zanres Ice Cream Bar next stop!)
Frosted, malted, or peppered and salted.
   Rah! Rah! Rah!
   (Ice cream soda on a ginger ale pop!)
   Oh, spumoni, oh, tortoni.
   And confidentially, no iced baloney.
I scream, you scream ... Rah! Rah! Ssss-ahh!

I scream, you scream,
We all scream for ice cream, Rah! Rah! Rah!
(Just one cornetto ~ or maybe duo ~)

ICE CREAM
Is this the last excitement of the day? That or a newspaper poke of chips were our family favourites as we shouted out the *Ice cream* chorus in the car on the way home.

(Zanres Ice Cream Bar in Forres made the BEST knickerbocker glories. But it's ok. I won't mind if you sing your top ice cream stop instead.)

MORNINGTOWN RIDE

Malvina Reynolds said of her song: 'I remember how it was when I was little. I know youngsters hate to go to bed at night because it seems like it is the end of the world. I wanted to help them understand that they were heading somewhere, when they got into bed, that they were heading for morning. And strangely enough, this song became a grown-up hit all over the world. It really amazed me.'

HUGS

For the end of a Grand Day Out.

29 MORNINGTOWN RIDE

Train whistle blowin' makes a sleepy noise,
Underneath their blankets go all the girls and boys.
Headin' from the station out along the bay,
All bound for Morningtown many miles away.
    Rockin' rollin' ridin' out along the bay,
    All bound for Morningtown many miles away.

Sandie's at the engine, Judy rings the bell,
Joan swings the lantern to show that all is well.
Rockin' rollin' ridin' out along the bay ...

Maybe it is raining where our train will ride,
But all the little travellers are snug and warm inside.
Somewhere there is sunshine,
    somewhere there is day,
Somewhere there is Morningtown many miles away.
    Rockin' rollin' ridin' out along the bay,
    All bound for Morningtown many miles away ...

30 HUGS

Tiny mice and teeny bats,
Little owls and kitten-cats,
Wiggly worms and baby bugs,
All their grandmas give them hugs.